Getting Started

Baby massage can be done at any time of the day. The best time to begin a massage is when your infant is in the *Quiet Alert State*. Many people like to massage before or after the bath. It is preferable to massage between feedings.

Which Type of Oil & Why?

Using oil on the skin helps avoid friction during massage. When Loving Touch® is used with newborns, oil may not be needed. However, studies conducted at the Touch Research Institute indicate that the use of oil had a better response than not using oil. Natural cold-pressed or organic oils, such as sweet almond, apricot, sesame seed or grape seed oil, will nourish your baby's skin and give a very smooth and pleasant feeling. Do not use mineral oil-based lotions, peanut oil or baby powder. Use of unscented oil is preferred because babies put their hands in their mouths and they also need to be able to recognize their mother's scent. If you suspect an allergy, you may want to perform a patch test. Place a small amount of the oil on your infant's wrist, leave for 20 - 30 minutes. Redness may indicate a reaction.

Massage Techniques & Sequence

The massage techniques are a combination of traditional Swedish, East Indian, Reflexology and Conditioned Relaxation Response™ (CRR). The overall sequence begins at the head, then the feet, tummy, chest, arms, face, back and finishes with gentle exercises.

Definitions: Touch is superficial or deep. Containment, stilling or grounding.

Gliding or Effleurage: Is applied horizontally on the muscle with varying amounts of pressure and is an important stroke for applying oil. Warms the muscle and is an excellent transitional stroke between other strokes. Includes feathering.

Pétrissage: Means to "knead" the muscle and is applied in a vertical position. Kneading lifts, squeezes and presses the tissue. A very good stroke for decreasing muscle tension. Fulling is a kneading movement.

Friction: Consists of small yet deep movements in order to flatten, broaden or stretch muscle in a specific area that warms up the muscle. May include, circular friction, rolling, wringing and vibration.

Vibration: Wakes up nerves and relaxes the muscle. Combing is a vibration movement.

Reflexology: Originated in China, Reflexology stimulates areas in the feet, hands and ears by applying pressure to various points. Also known as "zone therapy."

Conditioned Relaxation Response: Combines a gentle shaking movement of the muscle with a verbal cue to relax. May be classified as rhythmic mobilization. Effective in relaxing muscle groups or an entire limb.

Table of Contents

Let's Begin

It's important to choose the right position. Floor time is the safest place and your baby can move around. Make sure you are comfortable and your back is supported when you perform the massage. With legs straddled, put the soles of your feet together. Spread your baby blanket over your outstretched legs. Your baby's head will rest comfortably before you. Position your baby in the eye-to-eye position. Check with your CIMI® about alternative positions.

Get in Tune and Ask Permission

Babies can feel your tension so before beginning, take in several deep breaths and relax your entire body. Cradle your baby's head in your hands, look into your baby's eyes, say her or his name and ask permission to begin. If the response is positive, rub your hands together in the universal sign of "Massage," and trace your fingers down the center of your baby's body. Begin the first massage stroking component for "Legs and Feet."

Amount of Pressure

The amount of pressure depends on your baby's age. Use a loving touch that provides some pressure. Studies reveal that infants have better neurological advantages when some pressure is applied. Avoid a ticklish touch.

How Long Should the Massage Last?

This varies according to the ability of the giver and the state of the awareness of your newborn. The average length of time is anywhere from 20-30 minutes; fewer minutes for a premature or a newborn. Babies will let you know if they are becoming overstimulated. They may get fussy. Follow your baby's cues.

Environment and Sounds

It's best to perform the massage with natural lighting in a warm location that avoids drafts. Use your blanket to swaddle your infant if she or he gets cold. Both of you will enjoy the massage if you are not distracted by too much excessive noise. Soothing music such as nature sounds or heartbeat sounds will add some additional relaxation.

Suggested Music:

Music for Dreaming CD : Features best loved lullabies like Brahms Lullaby, Hush-a-bye-baby and Golden Slumbers. Rhythm is the heart of all music. "The rhythm of this music replicates the human heartbeat, and the tempo is that of the resting human pulse to bring about a sense of calm." - Cherie Ross, Sound Impressions, Australia

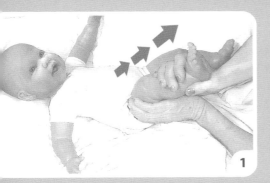

1. INDIAN MILKING ~ of the whole leg from the upper thigh to ankle
Gliding : Use the entire palmar surface of the hands in gliding strokes pull away from the heart. Form the hand into a letter "C" and, with the thumbs facing downward, wrap the fingers around the leg and glide outward in long, sweeping strokes towards the foot.

> NOTE : Talk to your baby. Tell him or her what you are doing. Ask them how it feels. Make eye contact and look for smiles.

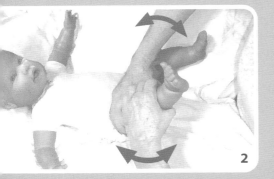

2. TURN AND CARESS ~ hands side-by-side
Wringing : With both hands turning opposite to each other, work your way from the thigh outwards toward the ankle and off the foot. Be careful not to twist the knee joint.

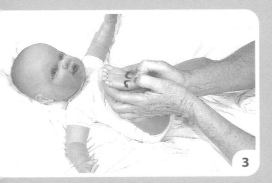

3. FANNING ~ on the bottom of the foot
Gliding and Circular Friction : Smooth the wrinkles out of the bottom of the foot using a thumb-over-thumb fanning-out stroke. Spread the toes apart. Kiss your baby's toes to open up.

4. ROLL EACH TOE ~ from the big toe to the little toe
Petrissage : As if you have a small pea between your finger and thumb, gently squeeze each toe and give a little pull. This is a good time to introduce a nursery rhyme, such as "This Little Piggy Went to The Market." (See page 14)

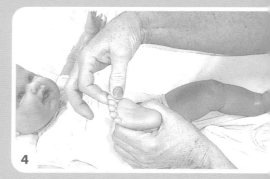

5. PRESSURE POINT THUMB WALK ~
Reflexology : Imagine five lines running up the heel of the foot to the toes. Walk thumbs up the bottom of the foot to include the surface under the toes. To get the toes to open, kiss the tops of the toes, wait a second or two, and then you can reach that area.

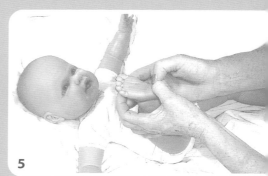

6. AIRPLANE RUNWAY ~ glide palm of hand off foot
Gliding : Using the palm of your hand, glide and stroke up and over the sole of the foot and off the toes while you wiggle your fingers and watch baby's reaction. Track 180 degrees left and right. Watch to see if your baby's eyes follow your hand movements.

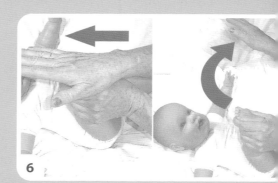

INTERNATIONAL
Loving Touch®
FOUNDATION INCORPORATED

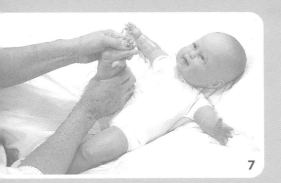

7. GENTLE STRETCHING OF THE FOOT ~

Joint movements : Cup your hand around the foot and place your thumb in the center sole of the foot. Now, flex and extend the foot. Gently rotate ankle in a circle. Place your other hand in a supporting position on the leg and give a gentle stretch.

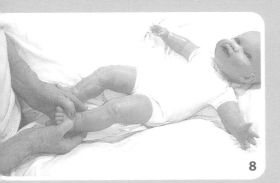

8. TOP OF FOOT AND THE ANKLES ~ finger pads

Gliding and Circular Friction : Move upward on the top of the foot between the small bones towards the ankle and make small circular friction movements around the ankle joint.

> NOTE : Indian milking is away from the heart for tension relief and relaxation. Swedish milking moves towards the heart for circulation and stimulation.

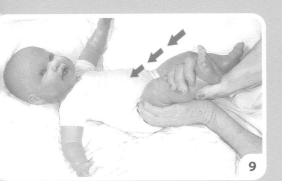

9. SWEDISH MILKING ~ of the whole leg from ankle to thigh

Effleurage : Glide up the leg toward the heart in long, alternating sweeping strokes. This will encourage blood flow back to the heart and improve lymphatic drainage. The top of the groin area is where the inguinal lymph node is located.

10. ROLLING THE LEG ~ ankle to thigh or the thigh to the ankle
Friction : Imagine you have a piece of Play-Dough® in your hand and you are making a Play-Dough® rope. Press your palms together and squeeze the muscle against the bone for improved circulation. For a toddler, this technique can be done by propping his or her foot against your shoulder and rolling the thigh. The movement can be gentle, but rapid. *NOTE: Sing to your baby, "Row, row, row your boat, gently down the stream."*

11. NERVE STROKE OR FEATHER STROKE ~ finishing stroke
Effleurage : This stroke is very light and superficial. From the thigh downward, gently stroke ever so lightly as if to say, "All done." It is interesting to observe, that this is the way the hair lies on the skin. This is a calming stroke. You may want to use containment, stilling, or grounding as an alternative to feather stroking. Follow your baby's cues.

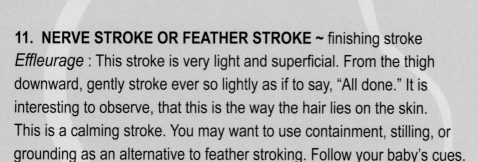

12. CONDITIONED RELAXATION RESPONSE (CRR) ~
Ryhthmic Mobilization : This consists of a gentle tapping and a jiggle of extremity to let go. Give infant a verbal cue to relax so they begin to identify the verbal cue and the tone of the muscle.

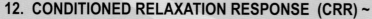

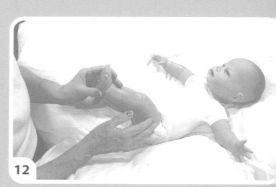

INTERNATIONAL
Loving Touch®
FOUNDATION INCORPORATED

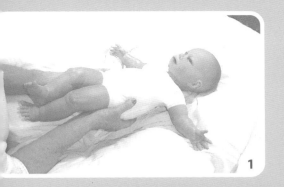

1. HANDS UNDER THE SACRUM ~

Joint Movement and Rocking : Cup the sacrum and buttocks in your hands, begin by gently rocking the lower extremities in a supportive manner. This loosens the abdominal muscles. Move one hand to the abdomen (like you are sandwiching your hands between the front and back) before proceeding to the paddling stroke.

> NOTE : It is advisable to massage on an empty stomach. Use an elevated position if the child has been diagnosed with Gastroesophageal reflux.

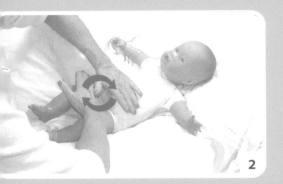

2. PADDLING DOWNWARD ~

Petrissage : Placing the palms of your hands on the baby's abdomen, make scooping strokes downward, stopping above the pubic bone. This resembles a water wheel going round and round.

> NOTE : Your hands should be placed below the sternum. Do not apply pressure to the base of the breast bone (xiphoid process).

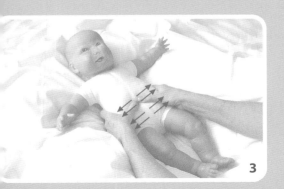

3. FULLING ~

Kneading : With thumbs together above the belly button in a midline position, but below the rib cage, gently grasp the muscle, lift and pull outward to baby's sides. Make two rows of strokes above the belly button, one row equal with, and two rows below, ending above the pubic area. If the umbilical cord is still intact, go around it with your fingerpads.

INTERNATIONAL
Loving Touch
FOUNDATION INCORPORATED

4. HANDS OF A CLOCK ~

Petrissage : In this stroke, one hand follows the other in a clockwise circle around the abdomen, tracing the intestinal tract. Stroke up the ascending colon, across the transverse, and down the descending colon. One hand should follow the other in a smooth, continuous movement. A newborn's abdomen may be an area of holding tension. Don't be surprised if your baby cries or gets uncomfortable. Be sensitive to this area and provide baby with a lot of support.

5. I LOVE YOU PETRISSAGE ~

Petrissage : Drawing the initials of the letter "I" down the descending colon, say "I." Then draw an upside-down "L" across the transverse and down the descending colon, and say "Love." Finally, draw an upside-down letter "U" up the ascending, across the transverse, and down the descending colon, saying "You." Put it all together and say, "I Love you!"

Reference: McClure, V. (1979). *Infant massage: A handbook for loving parents*. New York Bantam Books.

6. RAINBOW FINGERS ~ walking across the tummy

Fulling : From the baby's right to left, walk your fingers in a "rainbow arch" fashion in several rows horizontally across the tummy. Avoid tickling. Do one walk above the belly button, one even with, and one below. If it appears that your baby is gassy or has constipation, repeat the strokes for the tummy several times a day, or use the colic routine. Include the knee to the tummy press.

INTERNATIONAL Loving Touch® FOUNDATION INCORPORATED

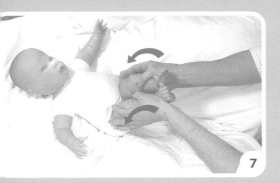

7. KNEE-TO-TUMMY PUSH ~

Passive Joint Movement : Placing your hands on the outside of your baby's thighs, including cupping the sides of the knees, gently push as a unit toward the tummy and hold for 3 to 5 seconds. Release and repeat movement.

> NOTE : *Avoid placing fingers behind the knees when pushing forward as this is a very sensitive area.*

8. ROCKING TUMMY ~

Centering Balance : Place palm of hand flat on tummy in a horizontal position and gently rock from side to side, or one hand may be placed under the back. Containment, stilling or grounding of the hands is also beneficial.

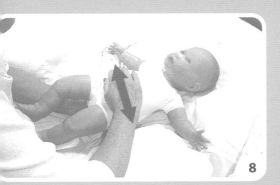

FOR RELIEF OF TUMMY CONCERNS ~

A gassy or colicky baby is both a frustration and a challenge. The following combination of stroking techniques can help to relieve and release discomfort. Combine the techniques and repeat 2 - 3 times a day for as long as three weeks.

COLIC ROUTINE
(Repeat Sequence 3 Times)
1. Paddling Downward
2. Knee-To-Tummy Push
3. Hands of Clock
4. Knee-To-Tummy Push

1. HELLO STROKE ~ in an outward movement

Effleurage : Begin by placing the palmar surface of your hands on the center of your baby's sternum, allowing them to mold to your baby's chest and smooth outward like you're smoothing the pages of a book. This may include stretching out the arms and dropping down on the side of the chest or rib area.

> NOTE : When massaging the chest area it is important to pace your breathing to your child's breathing.

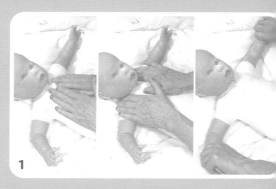

1

2. HEART OF LOVE ~

Effleurage : Stroke up the sternum around the top of the chest and down in a heart-shaped movement, being careful not to press deeply at the base of the breast bone. Your fingerpads may extend over the tops of the shoulders and around the sides of the ribs. Use your full palm. Repeat this movement several times.

2

3. BUTTERFLY OR CROSS THE HEART ~

Effleurage : With the palmar surface of your hand, use a gliding stroke from the top of one hip upward to the infant's opposite shoulder. Then, using the other hand, glide from the other hip to the other shoulder. Glide one hand all the way up and down before gliding the opposite hand up and down. This should be done in a very rhythmical way, flowing from the base of your spine in almost a rocking movement.

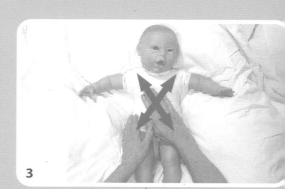

3

INTERNATIONAL Loving Touch® FOUNDATION INCORPORATED

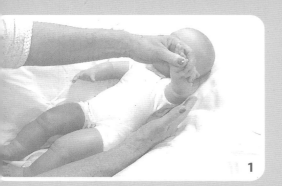

1. CONDITIONED RELAXATION RESPONSE (CRR) ~

Ryhthmic Mobilization : Begin by holding your baby's arm in your hand and gently pat, tap, or jiggle the back side of the arm to encourage the arm to release and extend. Give a verbal cue to relax so the infant begins to identify the verbal cue with the tone of muscle.

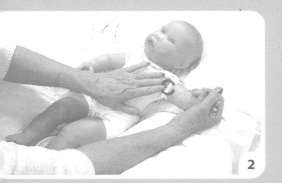

2. AXILLA AREA ~ small circles in arm pit

Circular Friction : With the pads of the fingers, gently make small circles in the armpit region. Do not poke or tickle. This stroke encourages lymphatic drainage. Be sensitive to the armpit area as this is where the axillary nodes are located.

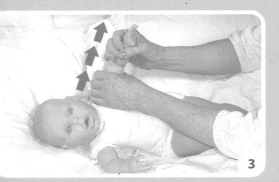

3. INDIAN MILKING ~ from shoulder to the wrist

Gliding : Use the entire palmar surface of the hands in gliding strokes away from the heart. Form the hand into a letter "C" and, with the thumbs facing downward, wrap the fingers around the arm and glide outward in long, sweeping strokes towards the hand.

INTERNATIONAL
Loving Touch
FOUNDATION INCORPORATED

4. TURN AND CARESS ~ hands side-by-side
Wringing : With both hands turning opposite to each other, work your way from the shoulder to the wrist and off the hand.

5. AIRPLANE RUNWAY ~ open the palm of the hand
Gliding : Gently stroke outward to the tips of the fingers. If the hand won't open, gently kiss the top of the clenched fist, wait a second or two, and the hand will open. Repeat the stroke.

6. ROLL EACH FINGER ~ open the palm of the hand
Petrissage : With finger pads, move up and down on each finger. As with the toes, gently move each finger around its axis and give a little pull. Kiss your baby's fingers and play a little game, or recite a nursery rhyme, like "Family Fingers." (See page 14)

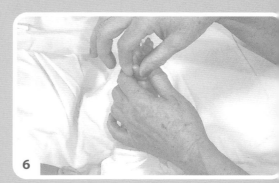

INTERNATIONAL Loving Touch® FOUNDATION INCORPORATED

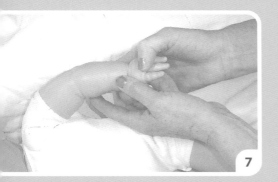

7. TOPS OF HANDS AND WRISTS ~

Gliding : Stroke upward on the top of the hand toward the wrist and small circular friction around the wrist joint.

> NOTE : Pay attention to your infants cues of engagement or disengagement. Infants respond in predictable ways and will let you know when they need time to rest. Do not overstimulate.

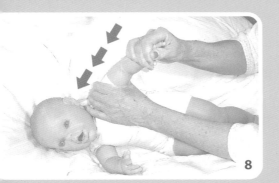

8. SWEDISH MILKING ~ from wrist to shoulder

Effleurage : Using the full palmar surface of the hand, glide up the arm toward the heart in long, alternating sweeping strokes to encourage blood flow back to the heart. The lateral stroking hand may sweep around the top of the shoulder.

9. ROLLING ~ from shoulder to wrist

Friction : Press your palms together around the arm and gently squeeze the muscle against the bone for improved circulation. In a toddler, this technique can be done by placing your child on their side as well. Imagine you have a piece of Play-Dough® in your hand and you are making a Play-Dough® rope. Move the hands rapidly back and forth.

10. NERVE STROKE OR FEATHER STROKE ~

Effleurage : This stroke is very light and superficial. From the shoulder outward, gently stroke ever so lightly as if to say, "all done." It is interesting to observe, that this is the way the hair lies on the skin.

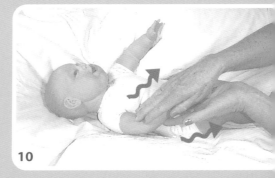

10

Massage Songs & Nursery Rhymes

(Songs to sing while you massage your baby)

"This Little Piggy Went to The Market" - (Legs & Feet)

This little piggy went to market,

This little piggy stayed home,

This little piggy had roast beef,

This little piggy had none.

And this little piggy went... Wee, Wee, Wee, all the way home!

(use different food words, pizza, veggie burger, brownies)

"Family Fingers" - (Arms & Hands)

This is the father, short and stout,

This is the mother with children all about

This is the brother, tall you see,

This is the sister with dolly on her knee,

This is the baby, sure to grow,

And here is the family, all in a row!

(Point to each finger in turn, starting with the thumb)

(Gently grasp baby's whole hand when done)

"Clap, Clap Song" - (Baby Exercises)

I take my little hands and go Clap, Clap, Clap

I take my little hands and go Clap, Clap, Clap

I take my little hands and go Clap, Clap Clap

Clap, Clap all day long!

(repeat with , I take my little Foot and go Tap, Tap, Tap, &

I take my litle hands and go Bye, Bye, Bye)

"Hinges Song" - (Baby Exercises)

I'm all made out of hinges and everything bends,

From the top of my head, way down to the end.

I'm hinges in front and I'm hinges in back,

If I didn't have hinges I surely would CRACK!

Music Suggestions: (www.lovingtouch.com)

Music for Dreaming CD's (1, II, III)

Baby-Go-to-Sleep Nursery Rhymes CD's (1, 2, 3)

INTERNATIONAL
Loving Touch®
FOUNDATION INCORPORATED

1. CRADLING BABY'S HEAD IN YOUR HANDS ~

Caressing Hold : With the palmar surface of the hands, cup your baby's head in your hands. Continue to seek permission and make good eye contact. Gently make small circles on the scalp, being careful of the soft cranial areas.

> *NOTE : The face may be very sensitive and an area of tension. If your baby doesn't like it at first, come back later.*

2. FLAT OF THE THUMBS ON FOREHEAD ~

Gliding : Place the thumbs together on the midline of the forehead and stroke outward toward the temple area. Make several outward strokes. Or you may cross over the midline with each thumb and glide outward toward the temple area.

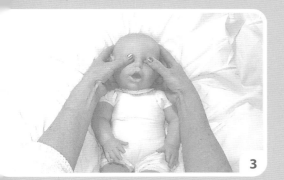

3. EYES ~ from the tear ducts across the eyelids

Gliding : Glide finger pads across the eyes laterally to close. With finger-pads, apply gentle circular friction in the tear duct area at the top of the nose. This is a good opportunity for engagement and "peek-a-boo" games.

4. CHEEKS ~ midline across the cheeks

Gliding : From the bridge of the nose, glide in an outward/upward lateral direction toward the temples. Continue to glide over the entire cheek area. At the base of the nostrils, make several circular friction movements with your fingertips.

5. SMILE FACE ~ upper and lower lips

Gliding : Move outward toward the temples and make a smile on your baby's face. Strokes may be administered in the opposite direction. Touching the cheeks during this stroke may trigger the rooting reflex. Do bilateral massage. *Note : Perform the movements in the opposite direction for infants with Down's syndrome, cleft palate, or feeding problems.*

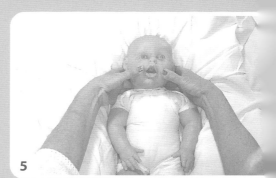

6. CHIN ~

Small Circular Friction : Using the fingerpads, with light pressure, "draw" small circles around the jaw line and under the chin. This is the cervical node area.

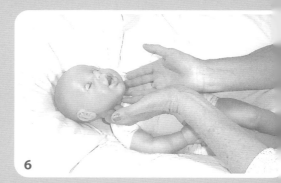

INTERNATIONAL
Loving Touch
FOUNDATION INCORPORATED

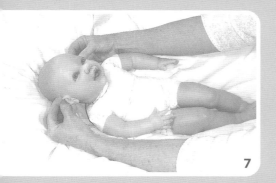

7. EARS AND NECK ~

Small Circular Friction : Knead the ears between your fingers and thumb. Use gentle gliding strokes around the back of the ear area and neck.

8. SMALL CIRCLES ON THE SCALP ~

Small Circular Friction : The pressure should be deep enough to feel the skin move over the bony cranium, but soft enough to be pleasurable.

NOTE : Do not apply direct pressure in the two fontanelle spaces. These are the normal membrane-covered soft places in the skull of a newborn. One is toward the front just behind the frontal bone that forms the forehead; the other is further back a couple of inches. Both soft places are on the front-to-back midline of the skull.

LOVING TOUCH BENEFITS FOR PARENTS & PRIMARY CAREGIVERS

- Helps the parent to feel more confident and competent in caring for their children.
- Gives parents the tools for understanding their infants/children's unique rhythms.
- Daily massage helps parents to unwind and relax.
- Provides a positive way for fathers to interact with their infants/children.
- Promotes bonding and attachment. Reinforces good eye contact.

INTERNATIONAL
Loving Touch®
FOUNDATION INCORPORATED

1. EFFLEURAGE ~ from shoulders to buttocks

Gliding : With the palmar surface of the hands, move down the back towards the buttocks. Repeat movement.

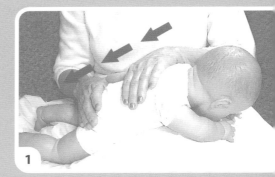

2. STREAMING ALTERNATELY ~

Friction - Wringing : With both hands, wring across the back alternately from the top of the spine to the tail bone. It is as if you are pulling the circulation up and over the spine. Do not press directly on the spine.

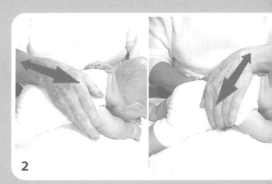

3. SWEEPING THE BACK ~ from the top of the shoulders to the buttocks

Effleurage : Place one hand grasping the buttocks with your fingers and thumb while the other hand flattens and glides down the back over the top of your base hand. The lower hand supports the base of the spine.

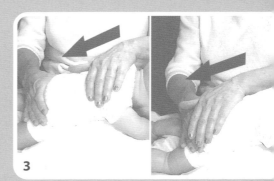

INTERNATIONAL
Loving Touch
FOUNDATION INCORPORATED

4. CIRCLES ALONG THE SPINE ~

Circular Friction : With the pads of the fingers, make small circular strokes along the spine, on one side and then the other side from neck to buttocks.

5. PETRISSAGE ~

Kneading : This stroke consists of circular kneading over the larger areas of the back from the tops of the shoulders and around the buttocks.

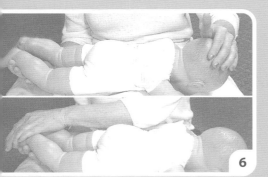

6. SWEEPING FROM HEAD-TO-TOE ~

Effleurage : In a full sweep from head to heels, stretch out your baby's legs. Stroke from head to heels. Close massage movements with effleurage strokes.

7. COMBING THE BACK ~

Vibration : Make your fingers like a rake and gently vibrate and comb your fingers from the back of the neck down the back to the gluteals buttocks, decreasing pressure. Repeat, end with rocking, containment, or stilling. Do not apply direct pressure to the spine. This completes the massage sequence.

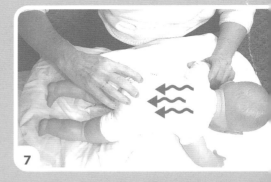

STRETCHING EXERCISES & BABY YOGA

At this time, you may continue to do gentle, passive stretching of the arms and legs. Your infant may be dressed for these exercises.

1. HUG-A-BABY ~

Joint Movements : Stretch the arms across the chest and gently press into your baby's body and say, "Right arm, left arm, hug myself." "Left arm, right arm, catch a little elf, did you catch him?"

2. ALTERNATE LEG AND ARM STRETCH ~

Joint Movements : Take the right hand and touch it to the left foot in the midline and wait until the baby sees the connection. Repeat several times on each side.

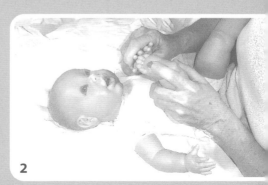

INTERNATIONAL Loving Touch FOUNDATION INCORPORATED